Trace and read the color words.

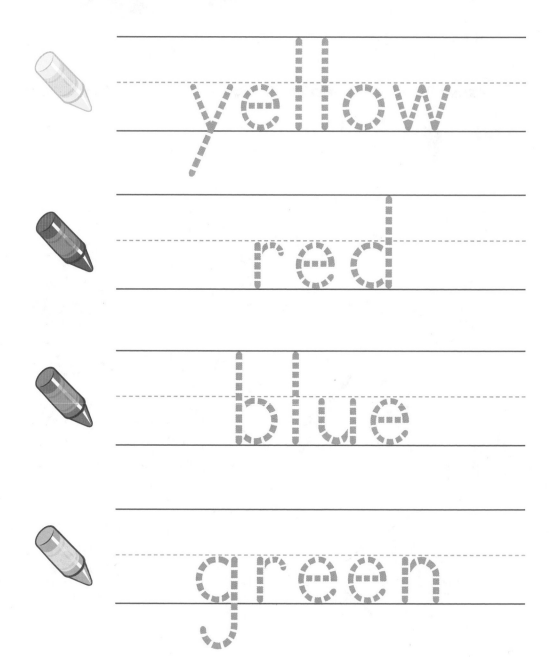

yellow

red

blue

green

1

yellow   red

Read the color words.
Color the picture.

blue   green

Read the color words.
Color the picture.

3

purple   brown

Read the color words.
Color the picture.

brown

purple

black

orange

Read the color words.
Color the picture.

A Fall Scene

 Look closely at the picture. Write the word to finish the sentences.

purple   brown

black   orange

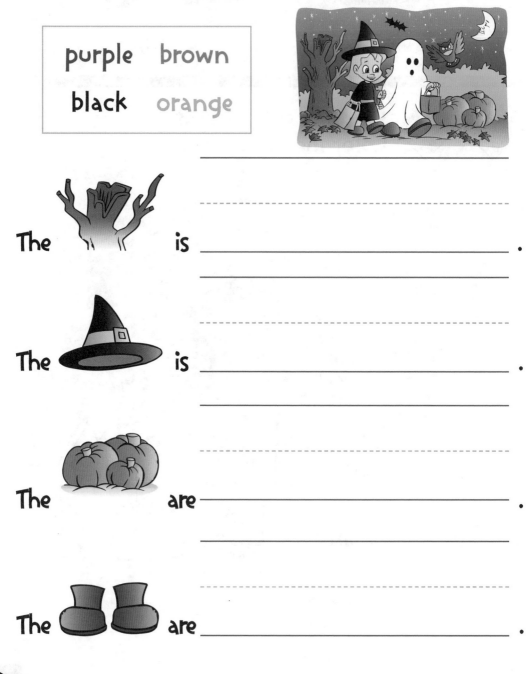

The ___ is _____ .

The ___ is _____ .

The ___ are _____ .

The ___ are _____ .

8

Use the color code to color the picture.

1 =   2 =   3 =

4 =   5 =   6 =

  Look closely at the picture.
Write the color word.

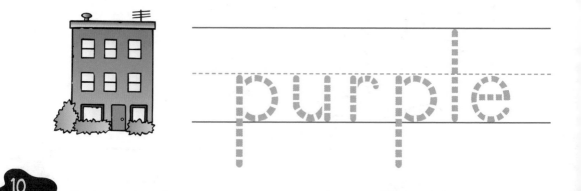

purple

brown   green   red   yellow

one
1
two
2
three
3
four
4
five
5

 Trace the number words.

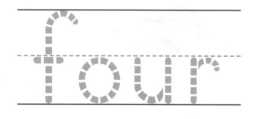

one

four

three

two

five

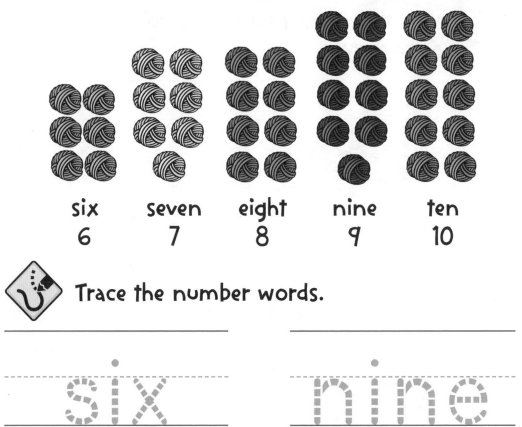

six	seven	eight	nine	ten
6	7	8	9	10

Trace the number words.

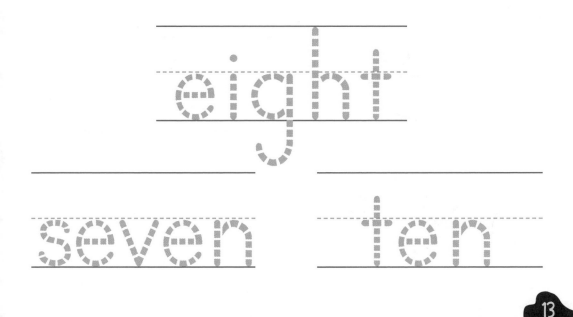

six

nine

eight

seven

ten

13

Write the number word next to the numeral.

1  _____

2 _____

3 _____

4 _____

5  _____

Sweet Shop

one	two	three	four	five
six	seven	eight	nine	ten

6

7

8

9

10

Follow the number words to draw the path to the treasure.

Animal Words

 Draw a line to the matching animal word.

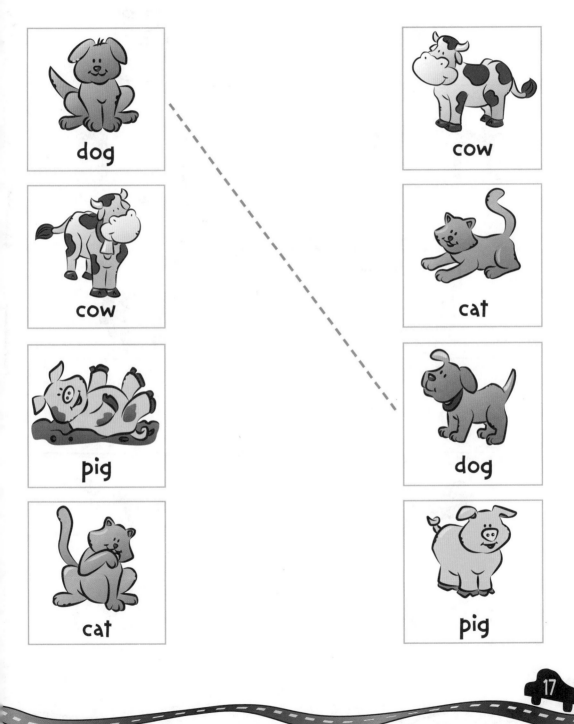

dog

cow

cow

cat

pig

dog

cat

pig

Write a to finish each word.
Read the word.

m a n

j r

Say the name of each picture.
Trace the word.

cat

van

bat

pan

18

This and That

 Draw what goes with each picture.
Trace and read the word.

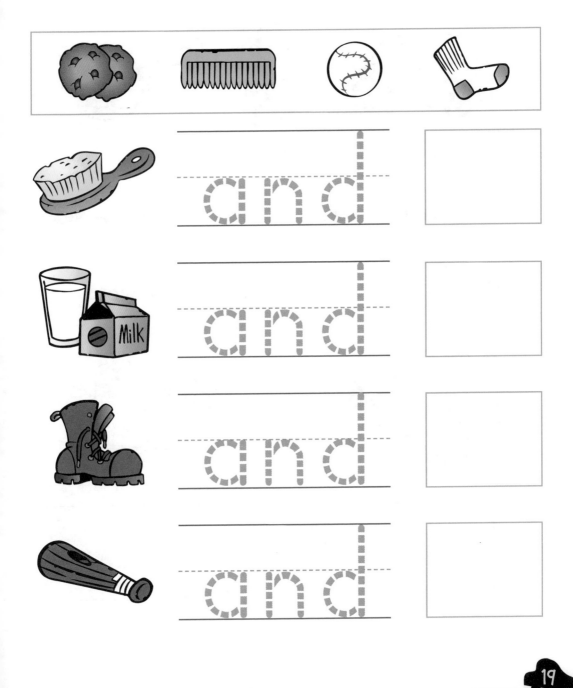

and

and

and

and

  Read the word.
Circle an in each word.

van   man   pan

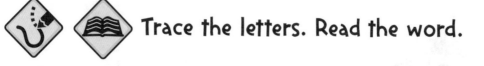

Trace the letters. Read the word.

fan   can

Trace the letter. Read the word.
Draw a line to the picture
it names.

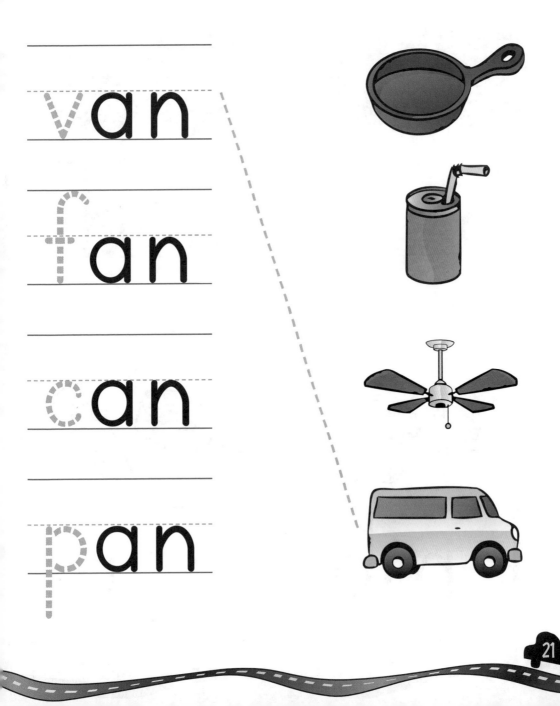

van

fan

can

pan

21

Trace a to finish each word. Read the word. Circle the picture it names.

bag

sad

lamb

pan

Short Ee

Write e to finish each word.
Read the word.

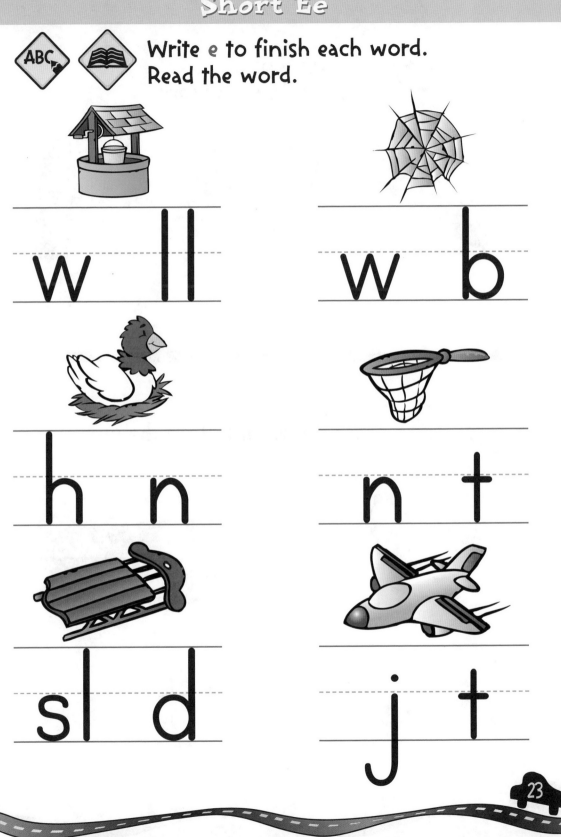

w _ ll

w _ b

h _ n

n _ t

s _ l d

j _ t

23

Read the word.
Circle en in each word.

pen   ten   men

Trace the letters. Read the word.

 hen    ten

Matching

 Trace the letter. Read the word.
Draw a line to the picture
it names.

men

ten

hen

pen

Trace Ee to finish each word.
Draw a line from each sentence
to the picture it names.

I met Ed.

Peg's pets.

26

Short Ii

Write i to finish each word. Trace the word. Circle the picture it names.

six

m tt

kck

h ll

27

Read the word.
Circle ig in each word.

wig   jig   dig

Trace the letters. Read the word.

pig   twig

28

Trace the letter. Read the word.
Draw a line to the picture
it names.

dig

wig

jig

pig

29

Fun with Ii

Say the name of each picture and circle the correct word. Write the word.

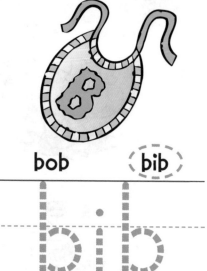

bob   (bib)

bib

mix   max

big   bag

had   hid

30

Write o to finish each word.
Trace the word. Draw a line
to the picture it names.

mop

t p

ck

s ck

31

Read the word.
Circle op in each word.

mop   hop   top

Trace the letters. Read the word.

STOP

stop   mop

Trace the letter. Read the word.
Draw a line to the picture
it names.

hop

pop

mop

top

33

Trace o to finish each word.
Draw a line from each sentence
to the picture it names.

Bob hops.

CLOCKS

Bob locks.

34

Write u to finish each word.
Trace and read the word.

s u n   n _ t

r _ g   j _ g

35

Read the word.
Circle ub in each word.

tub   sub   rub

Trace the letters. Read the word.

cub   sub

Trace the letter. Read the word.
Draw a line to the picture
it names.

tub

rub

sub

cub

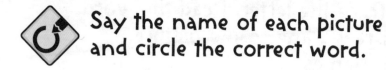

Say the name of each picture and circle the correct word.

(cut)   cot

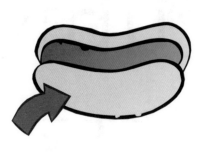

bin   bun

cap   cup

bug   bag

Say the name of each picture.
Write the letter to finish each word.

cl __ ck

c __ t

b __ g

n __ t

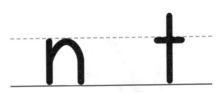

p __ g

m __ p

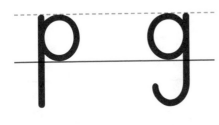

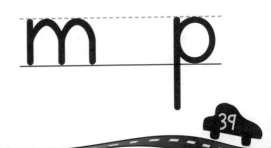

39

Animal Friends

 Trace the word that goes with each picture.

cat

dog

duck

hen

40

Look closely at the picture. Write the word to finish each sentence.

One _____ is in a _____ .

The _____ has a _____ .

A ⬭ is on the _____ .

41

bird   fish   pig

 Write the names of the winners.

_____

- - - - - - - - - - - - - - - -

_____

_____

- - - - - - - - - - - - - - - -

_____

_____

- - - - - - - - - - - - - - - -

_____

Read the words. Trace the words.

me

you

Trace the words.
Read the words.

me and you

you and me

Trace the word that goes with each picture.

 man  woman

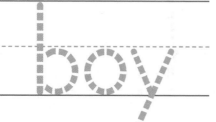 boy 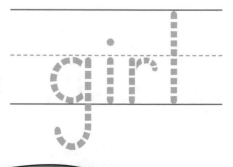 girl

Look closely at the picture. Write the word to finish each sentence.

_____

A _____ is on the .

_____

A _____ has the .

_____

The _____ is on a .

_____

The _____ has on.

45

📖 Read the words.

him

her

it

✏️ ABC Write the word to finish each sentence.

He gave a 🎁 to _____ .

She gave a 🎁 to _____ .

He gave a 🦴 to _____ .

Read the words.
Trace the words.

can   not

is   what

Find and circle each word
in the puzzle.

| can | not | is | what |

c a n e
m i s c   n w h a t
b n o t

47

Signs

Look closely at the signs.
Trace the words.

go

stop

Write the correct word below each picture.

48

 Trace the words. Read the words.

sun

tree

can

seed

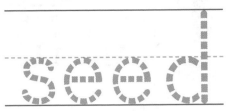

49

 **Read the words. Trace the words.**

first

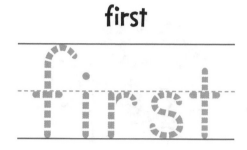

next

last

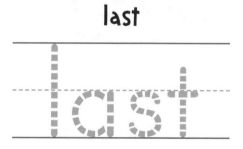

Telling a Story in Order

 Write the word to show the correct order.

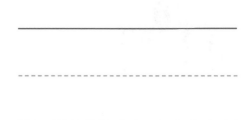

first

51

 Read the words. Write the words.

pour

mix

roll

bake

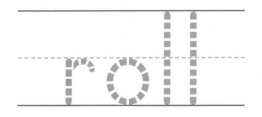

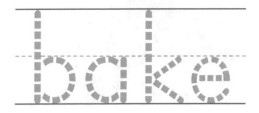

Bob's Birthday Party

Read the words.

sing   wish   eat

Write the word to finish each sentence.

The boys _____.

Bob makes a _____.

The boys _____.

53

 Trace the words. Read the words.

sit

run

fly

ride

 Trace the words. Read the words.

push

sleep

pull

jump

Read the words.

cut   write   read   paste

ABC Write the word to finish each sentence.

I use ✂ to _____ .

I use a 📕 to _____ .

I use GLUE to _____ .

I use a ✏ to _____ .

Pumpkin Fun

Use the code to color the picture.

write =   read =   cut =

write

write

cut

cut

read

cut

read

cut

Trace the words. Read the words.

little

sad

big

happy

sad   happy

little   big

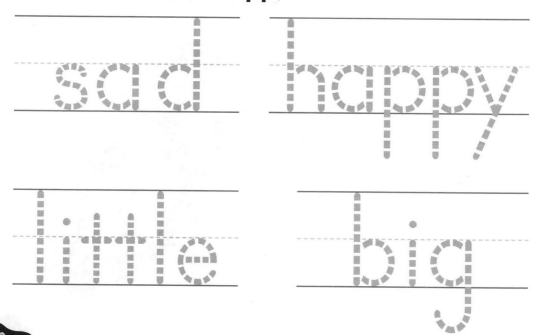

Circus Fun

 Read the words. Color the picture.

hide

go

jump

play

ride

Write the correct word below each picture.

_____

- - - - - - - - - - -

_____

_____

- - - - - - - - - - -

_____

Opposites

Read the words. Draw lines between the opposites.

hot

new

tall

cold

old

short

62

Read the words. Draw lines
between the opposites.

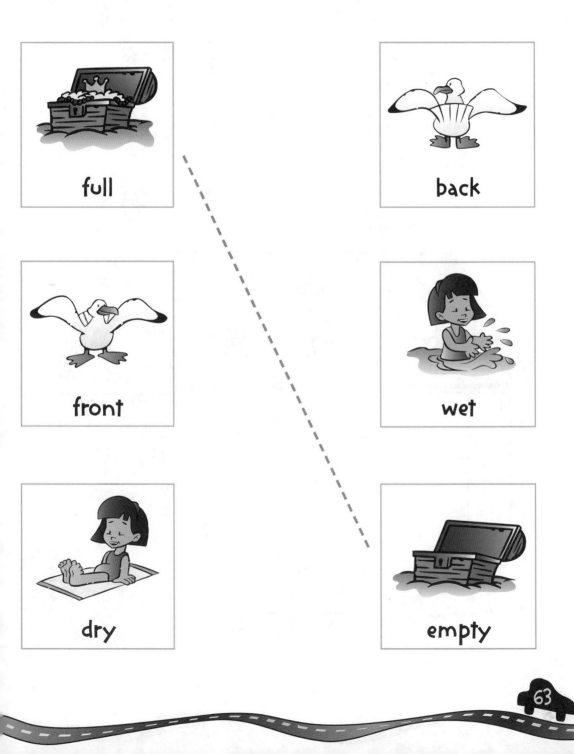

full

back

front

wet

dry

empty

ABC Write the words in the puzzle.

ACROSS →

1.

4.

5.

DOWN ↓

1.

2.

3.

girl   bird   boy

dog   frog   pig

1.   2.

3.

4.

Home
Tweet
Home

5.

64